Key Stage 3
Developing Literacy

WORD LEVEL

SPELLING ACTIVITIES FOR LITERACY LESSONS

year
8

Ray Barker and Christine Moorcroft

A & C BLACK

Contents

Published 2003 by A & C Black Publishers Limited
37 Soho Square, London W1D 3QZ
www.acblack.com

ISBN 0-7136-6481-9

Copyright text © Ray Barker and Christine Moorcroft, 2003
Copyright illustrations © Kirsty Wilson, 2003
Copyright cover illustration © Paul Cemmick, 2003
Editor: Lucy Poddington

The authors and publishers would like to thank Claire Truman for her advice in producing this series of books.

A CIP catalogue record for this book is available from the British Library.

Printed in Great Britain by St Edmundsbury Press Ltd, Bury St Edmunds, Suffolk.

A & C Black uses paper produced with elemental chlorine-free pulp, harvested from managed sustainable forests.

Introduction

Key Stage 3 Developing Literacy: Word Level is a series of photocopiable resources for Years 7, 8 and 9, designed to be used during English lessons or in other subjects across the curriculum to help with the spelling of key terms and new words. They are also ideal for homework. The books focus on the Word level strand of the Key Stage 3 National Strategy *Framework for teaching English: Years 7, 8 and 9*.

Each book supports the teaching of English by providing a series of activities that develop essential literacy spelling skills. Literacy, of course, includes more than these basic skills, but language is about communication, and the ability to spell words accurately is essential in creating meaning. Writers need to develop spelling strategies which they can use with confidence – leaving them free to concentrate on developing, arranging and constructing ideas.

Spelling in English is not easy because English includes words and language conventions from many languages and cultures. However, English spelling is not as irregular as it may appear: many of the exceptions to the rules share spelling patterns with other words, and can be linked to a common root word or language. **Word Level Year 8** provides revision and consolidation of spelling rules and exceptions, but also encourages pupils to develop skills and strategies which are progressive and transferable. These include:

- splitting words into syllables;
- being aware of phonemes and the variety of ways in which they can be spelled;
- finding words within words;
- using mnemonics to help memorisation;
- investigating the derivation of root words, prefixes and suffixes;
- using the Look, Say, Cover, Write and Check strategy.

How to use this book

Each double-page activity in this book is based around a Year 8 Word level objective. The left-hand page is a **starter** activity, which may be an OHT for use with the whole class, or an activity for the pupils to work on in pairs or small groups. The right-hand page provides a **consolidation** activity to reinforce the main teaching objective, followed by an **extension** activity (**Now try this!**) to reinforce and develop the pupils' learning.

Starter activities

Each starter activity is designed to be used as a short introduction to the consolidation activity that follows it. Evidence has shown that lessons which start with a sharp focus on a specific objective – for only ten to fifteen minutes – grab the pupils' attention and ensure that the whole class is clear about what to do and about the expected outcome of the lesson. The starter activities in this book address the objectives in a direct and explicit way. They involve both reading and writing, and encourage fast-paced learning and interaction. A range of teaching and learning styles are used – from independent to teacher supported – focusing on the following key teacher interactions:

- direction
- modelling
- explanation
- exploration
- discussion
- demonstration
- scaffolding
- questioning
- investigation
- reflection and evaluation.

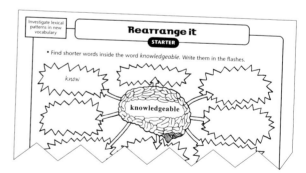

The starter activities in this book also provide valuable opportunities to revise previous learning. New terms are introduced and other important terms are revised during the starter activity; these are highlighted by being boxed or set in bold type. All the highlighted terms are explained in the glossary on page 64, which can be photocopied for the pupils to file and use for reference.

The starter activities can be photocopied and used in the following ways:

- as an OHT for whole-class teaching, with pupils giving answers orally or coming to the front to help complete the sheet;
- as a group activity, with each group working through the sheet or with different groups focusing on different parts of the sheet;
- as a timed activity, with the pupils completing as much of the sheet as possible within a time limit;
- in conjunction with appropriate class texts to help illustrate a principle;
- as preparatory work for an investigation, to be carried out for homework;
- as a stand-alone revision sheet for groups or individuals;
- as a tool for assessment.

Consolidation activities

The *Framework for teaching English: Years 7, 8 and 9* advocates that lessons should continue with a development of the main teaching points. The consolidation activities in this book can be used as the focus of this development, freeing teachers to work intensively with groups or individuals on the current objective.

The instructions in the activities are presented clearly to enable pupils to work independently. There are also opportunities for the pupils to work in pairs or groups, to encourage discussion and co-operation. A dictionary icon reminds pupils of the importance of checking their answers in a dictionary. Hints and reminders are given in boxes at the page margin.

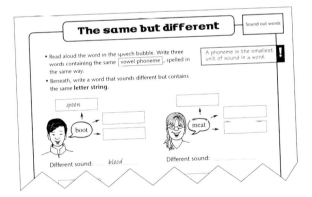

Encourage pupils to compile individual spelling logs by listing words they frequently misspell, identifying the problem areas of each word and writing down strategies to help them remember how to spell it. They should regularly review their progress by ticking off the words which no longer cause problems and by highlighting those that need further attention. Encourage the pupils to refer to their spelling logs as they write.

Extension activities

Each page ends with a **Now try this!** extension activity. These more challenging activities may be appropriate for only some of the pupils; it is not expected that the whole class should complete them. The pupils may need to record their answers in a notebook or on a separate piece of paper.

Organisation

The pupils will need access to a range of dictionaries (including etymological ones) and thesauruses. ICT facilities will also be useful for research into word derivations. Spell-checkers can be valuable but the pupils need to be aware that they cannot be used in examinations and that they do not check for homophones. The pupils should also remember that some spell-checkers use American spelling and grammar (this can be a useful teaching point for the differences between English and American English).

All the activities in this book are linked closely to the requirements of the *Framework for teaching English*, but it is not intended that they should be presented in any specific order, unless stated. This resource is versatile and is intended for teachers to use according to the literacy needs of their pupils.

Some of the activities can be linked with work in other subjects; however, it is envisaged that most of the activities will be carried out during English lessons.

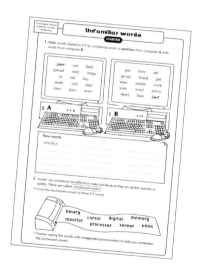

Teachers' notes

The notes provided at the foot of the activity pages contain additional instructions for using the sheets. These can be masked before photocopying. The notes on pages 6–9 offer further practical advice on making the most of the activity sheets, including extra teaching ideas, suggestions for applying the work to texts the pupils are studying, and answers to selected activities.

Teachers' notes

The notes below expand upon those provided at the foot of each activity page. They give ideas for making the most of the activity sheets, including suggestions for introducing the teaching objectives and for follow-up work based on the sheet.

Spelling

Foul vowels (pages 10–11). This revision exercise reinforces the point that the same sound can be made up of different letter combinations. This is because many words in English are taken from other languages, and follow the patterns and rules of their original languages. In the **starter** activity the pupils should notice which are the most common ways of spelling the vowel phonemes and which are exceptions. Analogy can be used to remember spellings of words spelled in the same way. The **consolidation** activity and the **extension** activity (**Now try this!**) investigate spellings of other phonemes and look at words which contain the same letters pronounced in a different way: for example, *meat, dead; boat, boar; spoon, blood.*

Plural patterns (pages 12–13). This activity involves revision of plurals rules. In the **starter** activity, the pupils sort words according to the ways in which their plurals are formed, including words ending in *s, ch, sh, x, f, o* and *y.* The **consolidation** activity develops this by asking the pupils to make their own rule list with examples. As a **homework** activity, the pupils could make up mnemonics to help them remember the exceptions to the rules, and words ending in *o* which take *es* (for example, *I dropped a bag of pot<u>atoes</u> on my <u>toes</u>*).

Peculiar plurals (pages 14–15). This activity deals with irregular plurals. The words in the **starter** activity are derived from Latin, Greek and Anglo-Saxon, and the plurals are made following the rules of those languages. The **consolidation** activity provides further examples, derived from Latin and Greek. However, many have been anglicised and two acceptable forms are often given in dictionaries (for example, *appendix – appendices/appendixes*). The pupils could be asked to investigate the origins of the words. Other words which have two possible plural forms include *fish – fish/fishes, buffalo – buffalo/buffaloes* and *zebra – zebra/zebras.*

Adding endings (pages 16–17). This activity revises suffixes and their impact on the spelling of a word. The **starter** activity looks at the suffixes *-ful* and *-ly.* In most cases, the addition of a suffix does not change the spelling of the root word, with the exceptions of words ending in *y* (for example, *beauty – beautiful*) and words ending in *le* (for example, *terrible – terribly*). When used as a suffix, *full* becomes *-ful*; no English word with a suffix ends with a double *l.* The **consolidation** activity reinforces learning with new examples and asks the pupils to consider the meanings of the words. Words such as *awful* and *dreadful* no longer mean 'full of awe' or 'full of dread', as their meanings have changed over time.

New beginnings (pages 18–19). This activity revises the use of prefixes to change the meaning of a word. The **starter** activity looks at common mistakes in the use of *al-* and *all.* Strictly, *all right* should always be written as two words, not as *alright. All together* means 'everyone together', whereas *altogether* is an adverb meaning 'entirely' (for example, *We were not altogether convinced by her argument*). The **consolidation** activity looks at common classical prefixes, while less well-known examples are provided in the **extension** activity. As a follow-up, the pupils could list words in other subjects that contain prefixes, such as maths and science words, and research the derivations.

This is the end! (pages 20–21). This activity reminds the pupils about word endings and their impact on spelling. In the **starter** activity, they investigate the way the vowel suffix *-ous* can change the spelling of a root word. It is interesting to note that words such as *humour – humorous* and *glamour – glamorous* revert to American spelling! The **consolidation** activity develops the work by looking at classical word endings and others from older languages such as Anglo-Saxon.

Apostrophe teasers (pages 22–23). The **starter** activity focuses on where to position the apostrophe in contractions such as *I'll* and *she'd.* The **consolidation** activity asks the pupils to correct the errors in examples of the apostrophe used in plurals or to show omission and possession. When dealing with possession, suggest that the pupils turn the phrases round, so, for example, *the girl's bag* becomes *the bag belonging to the girl*, and *the horses' mouths* becomes *the mouths of the horses.* This technique can help the pupils to work out where to place the apostrophe: it always comes after the final letter of the phrase (in these cases the *l* of *girl* and the *s* of *horses*).

Spot the difference (pages 24–25). This activity revises homophones – words that sound the same but have different spellings and different meanings. The **starter** activity is a 'race' activity which pupils should not find difficult. The **consolidation** activity asks them to find homophones and check their meanings. More sophisticated examples are provided in the **extension** activity, where an awareness of grammar is essential in order to distinguish between *practice/practise, licence/license* and so on. The *c* in the word denotes a noun; the *s* denotes a verb. The difference in pronunciation between *advice* and *advise* is a useful way of remembering this. The pupils could look in texts they are studying to find further examples of homophones.

Rearrange it (pages 26–27). Having fun with words is a good way for the pupils to investigate spelling patterns in terms of letter combinations and sounds. The **starter** and **consolidation** activities encourage pupils to find words within words, and to rearrange letters to make new words. This work can be linked with the use of mnemonics. The **extension** activity shows how analogy is useful when learning new vocabulary; words such as *notation, notion* and *oration* all have the common letter string *tion*. The pupils should carefully note exceptions to the spelling pattern, such as *torsion*.

Say the word (pages 28–29). This activity encourages the pupils to look for patterns in words to help with spelling. The poem in the **starter** activity shows why caution is needed when using analogy as a spelling strategy. Spelling irregularities have arisen because of the range of languages brought by invaders and settlers and the variety of new words entering the English language. The **consolidation** and **extension** activities look at the *ph* sound and the silent *h* before a vowel. Many words containing *ph* come from Greek. The silent *h* always comes before a vowel, and often after a *w*. Many *wh* words have homophones (for example, *whales/Wales, whine/wine*); an awareness of this will encourage the pupils to consider which is the correct spelling for the context.

Single or double? (pages 30–31). In this activity, the pupils investigate words containing single and double consonants. Words that pose a problem should be recorded in personal spelling logs. The **starter** activity concentrates on high-frequency and subject words that are often spelled incorrectly, such as *disappear, interruption* and *resource*. The activity shows how identifying prefixes and roots can help with spelling. The **consolidation** activity includes some more difficult examples. In the **extension** activity, the pupils revise two-syllable words which double the final consonant when a suffix is added (see pages 36–37).

Double act (pages 32–33). The words in this activity contain two sets of double letters. The answers to the **starter** activity are: *accommodation, embarrass, possession, occurrence, committee, address, assassin, aggression, succeed, commission, quarrelling, assessment*. Most of these have to be learned individually, but some follow rules: for example, *committee* comes from *commit*, which has the stress on the second syllable and therefore doubles its final consonant with a vowel suffix. The **consolidation** activity focuses on strategies for learning commonly misspelled words. The **extension** looks at words which follow a rule (see pages 36–37). Note how the change of stress in examples such as *refer – referring – reference* affects the spelling.

Spelling strategies

i before e? (pages 34–35). This activity focuses on *ie* and *ei* spellings and reinforces that the rule '*i* before *e* except after *c*' works only when the words contain a long *ee* sound. The **starter** activity looks at the spelling patterns in *ie* and *ei* words and introduces the variety of vowel sounds these letters can make. The **consolidation** activity develops this with new words and exceptions. It encourages the pupils to sound out words and not to take it for granted that the same letter combination will always make the same sound.

Stressed out! (pages 36–37). In this activity, the pupils investigate how the stress in polysyllabic words affects whether or not they double their final consonant when a vowel suffix is added. To revise the rules concerning the doubling of final letters, use examples such as *run – running* and *hit – hitting*. The doubling occurs in words of one syllable where a short vowel precedes a single final consonant. Ask for other examples to reinforce the rule. The **starter** and **consolidation** activities establish the pattern for polysyllabic words. If the final syllable of the word is stressed, the final consonant usually doubles when a vowel suffix is added (for example, *forget – forgetting*). If the first syllable is stressed, the general rule is that the final consonant does not double (for example, *happen – happened*), but exceptions include most words ending in *l* (for example, *travel – travelling*) and others such as *worship – worshipping*. The addition of a consonant suffix usually has no effect on the spelling of a root word. The **extension** activity looks at exceptions to the doubling rules.

-ible or -able? (pages 38–39). There is a rule for the use of these two suffixes, but the pupils must be aware that there are many exceptions. The **starter** activity establishes the rule: complete root words are more likely to take the suffix *-able* and incomplete roots tend to take *-ible*. The **consolidation** and **extension** activities encourage the pupils to investigate exceptions and to find other spelling patterns. Words such as *changeable* and *irreplaceable* do not drop the final *e* of the root word in order to avoid making a hard *g* or *c* sound. Other words such as *likeable* and *sizeable* retain the final *e* so that the root word can easily be recognised.

Should 'e' stay? (pages 40–41). This activity looks closely at words ending in *e*. The addition of a final *e* to single-syllable cvc words with short vowels makes the vowel sound long (for example, *fat – fate*). When adding vowel suffixes, the final *e* is usually dropped to avoid creating an awkward letter combination, such as *-eing*. However, this is not the case with consonant suffixes (for example, *lone – lonely*). The **consolidation** activity provides further examples and looks at exceptions where the *e* is retained to distinguish between different root words (for example, *dyeing/dying*) or to ensure that the root word remains recognisable (for example, *hoeing*). Other words, dealt with in the **extension** activity, keep the final *e* in order to avoid making a hard *c* or *g* sound (this does not apply to suffixes beginning with *e* or *i* since these vowels do not 'harden' a preceding *c* or *g*).

Book of words (pages 42–43). Use this activity to build on dictionary work, focusing on alphabetical order skills and using a range of dictionaries. In the **starter** activity, the derivations of *umpire*, *witness* and *scout* are partly or entirely incorrect. If groups use the Internet for research, ask them to compare the use of the ICT medium with printed books and to discuss advantages and disadvantages. In another lesson, the pupils could make cards for a similar word derivation game to be played in class (words derived from people's names are easiest). The **consolidation** activity focuses on alphabetical order beyond the initial letter. As a follow-up to the **extension** activity, ask the pupils to select a passage from a text they are studying and to replace some of the words with synonyms. They can then consider the effect this has.

The same but different (pages 44–45). This activity looks at words in which the same letter string is pronounced in different ways. The **starter** activity encourages the pupils to build words from a common letter string. Analogy, with the help of rhyme, can make words with common letter strings easy to spell. However, in other words the same letter string can make a different sound. The surrounding letters often influence the sound, and some words have the sound of the language from which they are derived (this is the case for many *ough* words). The **consolidation** and **extension** activities provide further examples, focusing on vowel phonemes.

Syllable splits (pages 46–47). In this activity the pupils revise splitting words into syllables as a strategy for spelling long words. The **starter** activity enables pupils to isolate each syllable in a 'window'. New words can be created by mixing and matching syllables. As a follow-up, you could ask pupils to invent nonsense words from the syllables and to find amusing definitions for them. Although the words may not be real ones, this is nevertheless a valid activity. The **consolidation** and **extension** activities help with the spelling of maths words and ask the pupils to consider a range of spelling strategies. Some pupils will respond more to the visual impact of words, and some to the sounds of words (see pages 48–49).

Memory test (pages 48–49). This activity looks at ways of memorising the critical features of words. The **starter** activity provides a range of strategies, some of which are visual and others auditory. Pupils who are visual learners will often associate words with shapes in terms of ascenders and descenders, capitals and lower-case letters. Other pupils may see common letter patterns or find words within words (for example, *temper* in *temperature*), which can be used to make written mnemonics. The **consolidation** and **extension** activities ask the pupils to apply the strategies to science and RE words.

Transform it (pages 50–51). This activity continues the work of the previous one, but takes the idea one step further: the pupils investigate the structure of words by changing letters and considering the impact on spelling and meaning. The **starter** activity provides fun transformational puzzles which encourage the pupils to consider word structures. The answers are: *none, cone, come, some; East, last, lest* (or *past, pest*), *West; wet, pet, pat, pay, day* (or *pry*), *dry; two, too, ton, son, sin, six; sick, silk, sill, sell, well; heat, head, held, hold, cold; dead, lead, lend, fend, find, fine, five, live; old, odd, add, and, aid, bid, bed, fed, few, new*. The **consolidation** activity looks at anagrams and how reorganising the letters of a word can change meaning and sound. The answers are: *blow – bowl;*

calm – clam; canoe – ocean; each – ache; heals – leash (or *shale*); *lemon – melon; owls – slow; palm – lamp; peach – cheap; pests – steps; phase – shape; robes – bores; save – vase; solve – loves; table – bleat; toga – goat; user – sure* (or *ruse*); *vowels – wolves; what – thaw; words – sword; wrong – grown; petal – leapt, plate* (or *pleat*); *smile – slime, miles* (or *limes*); *steal – least, slate* (or *stale*); *stripe – ripest, priest*.

Speak Anglo-Saxon! (pages 52–53). This derivation activity looks at words from Anglo-Saxon. It increases the pupils' awareness of the range of influences on the English language (which help to explain some of the eccentricities of spelling). The **starter** activity encourages the pupils to recognise the derivation of place names containing Anglo-Saxon elements. The Anglo-Saxon words in the **consolidation** and **extension** activities should be obvious if they are spoken phonetically: *boc – book; brun – brown; grene – green; mete – meat; milc – milk; modor – mother; waeter – water; beatan – beat; witan – wit; beran – bear.* **Now try this!** *abbod – abbot; biscop – bishop; cirice – church; flocc – flock; godsibb – gossip; hund – hound (dog), hus – house; twa – two; werold – world; wivan – wives.* The pupils are also asked to investigate the range of prefixes and suffixes which Anglo-Saxon has contributed to the modern English language.

That's a new one! (pages 54–55). This activity considers how new words are brought into our language and how the meanings of words can change to describe new objects or concepts. The **starter** activity looks at the different ways in which new words can be created: for example, by combining two existing words (*emoticon = emotion + icon*) or from acronyms (*radar*). The **consolidation** and **extension** activities focus on words which have changed their meaning over time. The older meanings of the words may remain in use or become obsolete. Encourage the pupils to find further examples of new words (or words which have recently acquired a new meaning) in texts they are studying, and to research the derivations. This could be linked with subject vocabulary, such as ICT.

Rhyme and reason (pages 56–57). Recognising a pattern in known words and applying this to new, unfamiliar words is 'using analogy'. This is seen in its simplest form in simple cvc words such as *cat*, *rat* and *sat*; these words are easy to spell because they all have the rhyming sound *at*. The **starter** activity takes a fun approach to rhyme. Cockney rhyming slang developed in the eighteenth and nineteenth centuries among East End

Londoners. Some of the words remain with us today: for example, people are said to 'rabbit on' (from *rabbit and pork – talk*). The answers are: *bacon and eggs – legs; plates of meat – feet; frog and toad – road; mince pies – eyes; north and south – mouth; skin and blister – sister; bread and honey – money; tea leaf – thief; whistle and flute – suit; baked bean – queen; Adam and Eve – believe; jam jar – car; currant bun – sun; butcher's hook – look; holy friar – liar; trouble and strife – wife; tomfoolery – jewellery; china plate – mate; dog and bone – phone; bricks and mortar – daughter.* The **consolidation** activity extends analogy to investigate a spelling pattern. The pupils need to be aware of exceptions when using analogy: for example, *plough* does not rhyme with *cough* even though the letter pattern is the same. As a **homework** activity, the pupils could make up their own rhyming slang: for example, *greasy chips – lips*.

High-frequency words

These activities look at strategies to spell difficult words encountered in the curriculum. The generic nature of the consolidation activity sheets enables them to be used for key words in any subject.

Troublesome words (pages 58–59). The **starter** activity focuses on high-frequency words that are commonly misspelled. It encourages the pupils to take one word at a time and look at a range of strategies for spelling it. The **consolidation** activity focuses on two strategies: derivation and finding words within words. These strategies can be used with the history words on page 62 and in conjunction with the strategies on page 63.

Unfamiliar words (pages 60–61). This activity makes pupils aware of the range of strategies available to them when faced with difficult, unfamiliar words. The **starter** activity uses words from ICT and shows two spelling strategies: identifying how words are made up and exaggerating the pronunciation of unstressed vowels. The **consolidation** activity encourages the pupils to try out a variety of strategies when learning to spell difficult or unfamiliar words.

On the subject (pages 62–63). Subject words need particular attention, since they can be technical and difficult. In the **starter** activity, the pupils create a bank of history terms to which they add more words. The **consolidation** activity focuses on three strategies: splitting words into syllables, writing mnemonics, and memorising critical features using the Look, Say, Cover, Write and Check strategy.

Foul vowels

STARTER

The same vowel sound can be spelled in different ways.

- Think of words that contain the same vowel sound as *ou* in *cloud*. Write them on the correct clouds.

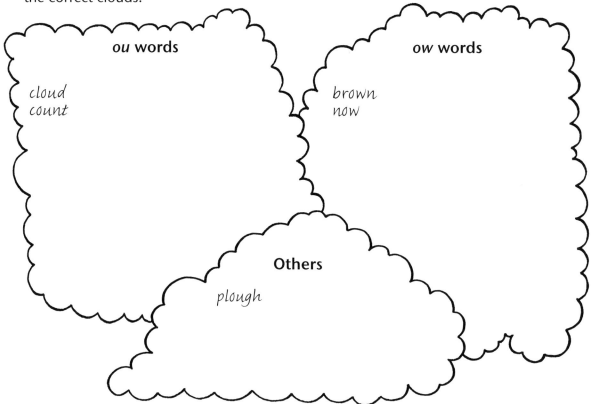

ou words

cloud
count

ow words

brown
now

Others

plough

- Think of words that contain the same vowel sound as *oor* in *door*. Write them on the correct doors.

or, ore and oor words

door
horn

aw words

paw
bawl

Others

roar

Teachers' note Split the class into small groups and give each group a copy of this page. Also photocopy the page onto an OHT. First revise vowels and practise saying and identifying them in a variety of words. Set a time limit of two minutes for the groups to list as many words as they can containing the same vowel sound as *cloud*. Then invite the groups to share their answers and to write them on the OHT. Discuss the different letter combinations which create the same vowel sound. Repeat the activity for the second vowel sound.

Developing Literacy
Word Level
Year 8
© A & C BLACK

Foul vowels

The vowel sound *ur* in *turtle* can be spelled in different ways.

- Think of words that contain the same vowel sound as *ur* in *turtle*. Write them on the correct cards.

ur words

turtle
burn

er words

term

ir words

circle

ear words

pearl

or words

worth

- Can the letter combinations make different sounds in other words? List examples.

ur _____ er _____

ir _____ or _____

ear _____

- For each of these words, list other words which contain the same vowel letters and are pronounced in the same way.
- Think of an exception (a word spelled in the same way but pronounced differently).

| main | meat | boat | spoon |

Example: *main, pain, rain and Spain all contain 'ai' and sound the same*
Exception: said

Teachers' note The pupils could work in pairs or small groups on this activity. During the plenary session, invite the pupils to share the words they have collected. Discuss different ways of spelling the same vowel sound, and different ways of pronouncing the same spellings.

Developing Literacy Word Level Year 8
© A & C BLACK **11**

Plural patterns
STARTER

• Cut out the cards. Sort them into sets of words which change from singular to plural in the same way.

Think of the singular form of each word.

!

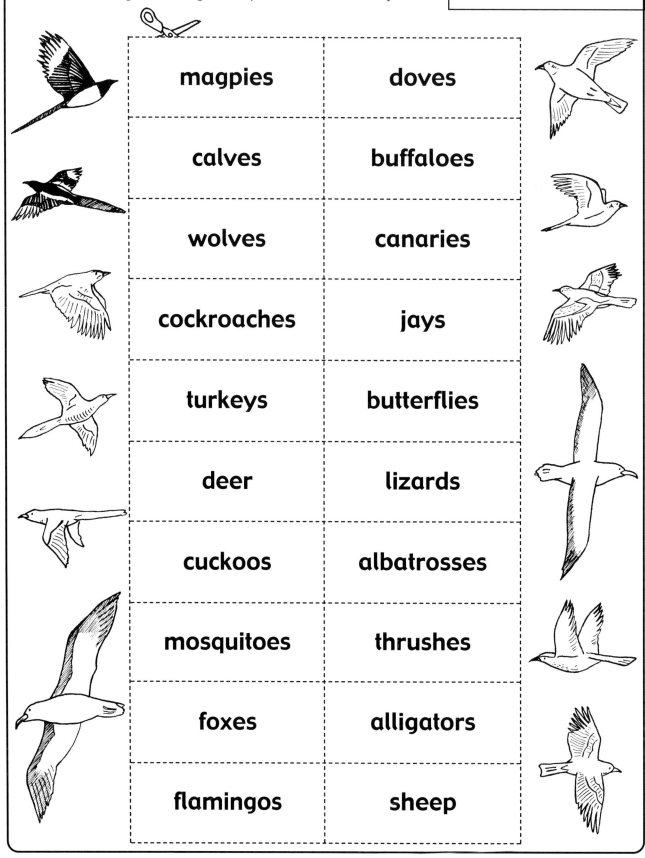

magpies	doves
calves	buffaloes
wolves	canaries
cockroaches	jays
turkeys	butterflies
deer	lizards
cuckoos	albatrosses
mosquitoes	thrushes
foxes	alligators
flamingos	sheep

Teachers' note Split the class into small groups and give each group a copy of this page. Set a time limit of three minutes for the pupils to sort the cards. Then discuss the different ways of forming plurals. Reinforce the rule for words ending in *y*: if the *y* is preceded by a vowel, just add an *s* (for example, *turkey – turkeys*). If the *y* is preceded by a consonant, the *y* changes to *i* before adding *es*. The rules for words ending in *o* also need reinforcement: some words take just *s* and others take *es*. Remind the pupils that some words are the same in the singular as in the plural.

Developing Literacy
Word Level
Year 8
© A & C BLACK

Plural patterns

- Complete the chart to show the rules for forming plurals. List examples for each rule. List exceptions to the rule, if there are any.

Give at least three examples for each rule.

Rules	Examples		Exceptions
	Singular nouns	Plural nouns	
1. Most nouns just add **s**	vampire bat graveyard	vampires bats graveyards	
2. Nouns ending with a **consonant + y** change			
3. Nouns ending with a **vowel + y**			
4. Nouns ending in **f or fe** change this to			
5. Nouns ending with **ch, sh, s or x**			
6. Nouns ending with a **vowel + o**			
7. Nouns ending with a **consonant + o**			

NOW TRY THIS!

- Draw another chart to show examples of:

nouns used only in the singular (for example, *music*)	nouns used only in the plural (for example, *scissors*)	irregular plurals (for example, *children*)

Teachers' note Encourage the pupils to think of exceptions to the rules, in particular for words ending in *f* and *o*. The completed sheet will provide a useful summary of all the work on plurals done this year and previously. It could be kept in a notebook, or a large copy could be made for display, so that the pupils can refer to it when writing.

Peculiar plurals
STARTER

Many words derived from other languages have irregular plurals. This is because the words follow the rules of their original language.

• Write the plural of each word.

• Write its language of origin.

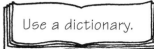
Use a dictionary.

Word	Plural	Origin
addendum	addenda	Latin
basis		
cactus		
child		
crisis		
criterion		
datum		
die		
foot		
formula		
fungus		
goose		
louse		
man		
mouse		
ox		
parenthesis		
sheep		
stimulus		
thesis		
tooth		
woman		

Teachers' note Split the class into small groups and give each group a copy of this page. Ask the pupils to find as many plurals as they can within a five-minute time limit (they will need access to good dictionaries). Different groups could work on different sections of the chart. Bring together the findings and discuss whether these irregular plurals follow the conventions of their original language (which may be very different from those which are familiar). Point out that some patterns can be established (for example, *addendum – addenda; datum – data*).

Developing Literacy
Word Level
Year 8
© A & C BLACK

Peculiar plurals

• Tick the correct plurals. There may be more than one correct answer.

Singular: **fungus**
Plural:
(a) funguses ☐   (b) fungae ☐
(c) fungus ☐   (d) fungi ☐

Use a dictionary. Find out the meanings of any unfamiliar words.

Singular: **radius**
Plural:
(a) radiuses ☐   (b) radia ☐
(c) radius's ☐   (d) radii ☐

Singular: **axis**
Plural:
(a) axis's ☐   (b) axi ☐
(c) axes ☐   (d) axises ☐

Singular: **hypothesis**
Plural:
(a) hypothesisis ☐   (b) hypothesii ☐
(c) hypothesis's ☐   (d) hypotheses ☐

Singular: **index**
Plural:
(a) indices ☐   (b) indexes ☐
(c) indexen ☐   (d) index's ☐

Singular: **appendix**
Plural:
(a) appendix's ☐   (b) appendices ☐
(c) appendi ☐   (d) appendixes ☐

Singular: **datum**
Plural:
(a) datums ☐   (b) datas ☐
(c) data ☐   (d) datum ☐

Singular: **medium**
Plural:
(a) mediums ☐   (b) media ☐
(c) medium ☐   (d) medias ☐

Singular: **phenomenon**
Plural:
(a) phenomena ☐   (b) phenomenae ☐
(c) phenomenons ☐   (d) phenomenes ☐

Singular: **criterion**
Plural:
(a) criteriones ☐   (b) criterions ☐
(c) criterium ☐   (d) criteria ☐

• Write about the patterns you notice.

_____

_____

_____

_____

_____

NOW TRY THIS!

These words have more than one possible plural.

• From the patterns you have described above, write what you think the plural forms might be.

Check your answers in a dictionary.

memorandum	hippopotamus	curriculum
matrix	cactus	vertex

Teachers' note Before beginning, explain that some words have more than one acceptable plural form. This is because our language is constantly changing and so plurals of words from other languages often become 'anglicised' (for example, medium – media/mediums). During the plenary session, review the answers and discuss whether these words are derived from Latin or Greek.

Adding endings
STARTER

- Add a suffix to make these words mean 'full of...' something.

hope

care

spite

beauty

wonder

doubt

- Think of other words that have this suffix. List them.

- Add *-ly* to the ends of these words.

Watch out for any changes in spelling. **!**

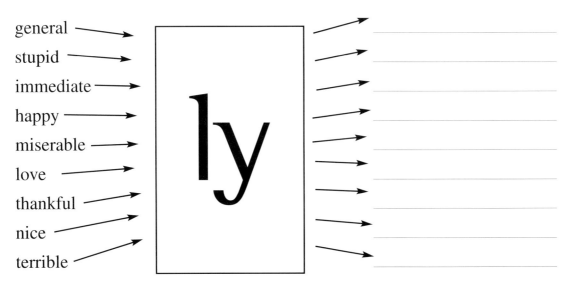

general

stupid

immediate

happy

miserable

love

thankful

nice

terrible

- Think of other words that have this suffix. List them.

Teachers' note Photocopy this page onto an OHT. Start the session by asking questions such as 'If you are full of hope, what are you?' (*hopeful*). Revise the term 'suffix' and ensure the pupils are aware that the suffix *-ful* has only one *l*. Invite pupils to write the new words on the OHT, and to notice any changes in spelling they need to make. Discuss that adding *-ful* changes the nouns to adjectives. Repeat this for the suffix *-ly* and point out that this suffix changes adjectives to adverbs. Note how in words such as *terribly* and *miserably* an ending of *-lely* would make a different sound.

Developing Literacy
Word Level
Year 8
© A & C BLACK

Adding endings

• Add the word *full* to the ends of these words. You may need to change the spelling.

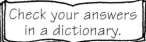
Check your answers in a dictionary.

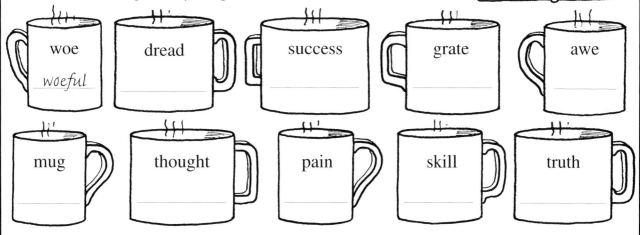

woe
woeful

dread

success

grate

awe

mug

thought

pain

skill

truth

• How does the spelling of *full* change when it is added to the end of a word?

_____

• Write about other changes in spelling you needed to make.

_____

• Write sentences using the words you have made.

Town's performance yesterday can only be

described as woeful.

Watch out! Some of them don't mean 'full of...' **!**

_____
_____
_____
_____
_____
_____
_____

NOW TRY THIS!

• Add the **suffix** *-ly* to these words.

crazy	especial	final	financial	grateful
lucky	possible	probable	simple	single

Check your answers in a dictionary.

• Write about any changes in spelling you needed to make.

Teachers' note During the plenary session, reinforce the idea that the word *full* always loses one *l* when used as a suffix. A double *l* is created when the further suffix *-ly* is added (for example, *hopefully*). Generally the spelling of the root word does not change when adding the suffix *-ful*, except in a few cases such as *skill – skilful, will – wilful* and *awe – awful*.

New beginnings
STARTER

• What happens when you use *all* as a prefix ? Write the new words.

all

mighty
most
ready
so
though
together
ways

• Write sentences to show the difference in meaning between these pairs of expressions.

We were all together, bored stiff.

I was altogether bored stiff.

all ways	
always	

all together	
altogether	

all ready	
already	

Teachers' note Photocopy this page onto an OHT. First revise the term 'prefix'. Invite the pupils to write the new words on the OHT, and to notice any changes in spelling they need to make. *All* loses one *l* when it is used as a prefix. Model this with pupils. Discuss how using *all* as a prefix changes the meaning as well as the spelling: for example, *all ways* (all the ways possible) does not mean the same as *always* (for ever).

Developing Literacy
Word Level
Year 8
© A & C BLACK

New beginnings

- Write at least two examples of words with these **prefixes**.
- From your examples, work out what each prefix means.

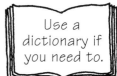

Use a
dictionary if
you need to.

Prefix	Words with this prefix	Meaning of prefix
anti-	*anticlockwise,*	
auto-		
bi-		
bio-		
circum-		
extra-		
micro-		
mono-		
multi-		
pre-		
semi-		
sub-		
super-		
trans-		

- On the blank rows, write three other prefixes you know. Complete the columns.
- Does the spelling of a word change when a prefix is added?

NOW TRY THIS!

- The prefixes below are more unusual. For each one, write:

  two examples of words containing the prefix

  what the prefix means

  which language it is derived from

  arch   demi   hypo   intra   pseudo   ultra

Teachers' note An etymological dictionary or access to the Internet will be useful for research. These are examples of classical prefixes (that is, from Latin or ancient Greek). Knowing their meanings will help the pupils to deduce the meanings of new words, as well as making spelling easier. During the plenary session, ask the pupils to share the other prefixes they have thought of.

This is the end!
STARTER

- Add the **suffix** *-ous* to these nouns to make adjectives.

Check your spelling in a dictionary.

Feeling adventurous? Try a bungee jump!

Noun	Adjective
adventure	*adventurous*
courage	
danger	
disaster	
glamour	
humour	
murder	

Noun	Adjective
ridicule	
right	
thunder	
treachery	
vapour	
vigour	
wonder	

- Decide which of these rules apply to the words you have made. Write the words on the correct notepads.

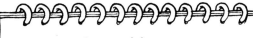

Just add *-ous*

Final *e* **is dropped**

Some final letters are dropped

e **is added**

Teachers' note Ask the pupils to work in pairs and give each pair a copy of this page. Also photocopy the page onto an OHT. Before beginning, revise the difference between a noun and an adjective, so that the pupils are aware of how suffixes can transform words from one word class to another. Set a time limit of four minutes for them to make as many of the adjectives as they can and check them in a dictionary. Then bring together their findings. Discuss the different ways in which the spelling of the root word is affected, and sort the adjectives onto the notepads.

Developing Literacy
Word Level
Year 8
© A & C BLACK

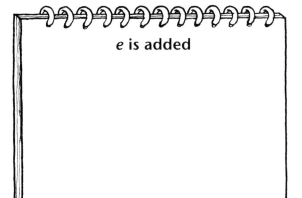

This is the end!

The word endings in the chart all come from other languages.

- Write at least two examples of words with these endings.
- From your examples, work out what each ending means.
- Use a dictionary to find out which language each word ending comes from.

Pleased to meet you. I am a Sagittarian vegetarian librarian.

Ending	Words with this ending	Meaning of ending	Origin
-arian	*vegetarian,*		
-cide			
-cracy			
-dom			
-ette			
-graph			
-itis			
-less			
-logy			
-naut			
-phobia			
-phone			
-scope			

- On the blank rows, write two other word endings that come from a foreign language. Complete the columns.

NOW TRY THIS!

Each set of words below has a common ending.

- Look up any unfamiliar words in a dictionary and write down their meanings.
- From the meanings of the words, write what each word ending means.

shipwright wheelwright playwright

tinware brassware earthenware

homeward seaward toward

bedside graveside riverside

alcoholic workaholic shopaholic

heatproof weatherproof waterproof

Francophile Europhile bibliophile

Teachers' note An etymological dictionary or access to the Internet will be useful for research. These word endings are derived from Latin and ancient Greek as well as Old English and French. Knowing their meanings will help the pupils to deduce the meanings of new words, as well as making spelling easier.

Apostrophe teasers
STARTER

• Write the apostrophe in the correct place in each word.

• Write the longer form of the word.

Remember to put the apostrophe where letters are missed out.

he would

he'd

	Longer form
h e'd	*he would*
s h e l l	
a r e n t	
d o e s n t	
w e l l	
i t s	
I d	
h a v e n t	
s h a n t	
w o n t	
d o n t	
s h e s	
t h a t l l	
h e l l	
w e r e	

	Longer form
I l l	
s h e d	
c a n t	
d o n t	
w e d	
y o u v e	
w o u l d n t	
w a s n t	
I v e	
h e s	
c o u l d v e	
h a d n t	
I m	
t h e r e s	
w h y s	

Teachers' note Photocopy this page onto an OHT. First revise the use of apostrophes to show omission and possession. Invite the pupils to read out each word on the OHT as it is printed, and then to write in the apostrophe, along with the longer form. They should notice the difference this makes to the sound of the word. Discuss why it is necessary to add apostrophes in these words and point out that without the apostrophes, some of the words mean something completely different (for example, *shell/she'll*). Ask the pupils how they knew where to place the apostrophe.

22

Developing Literacy
Word Level
Year 8
© A & C BLACK

Apostrophe teasers

- Read these signs and advertisements. Underline words in which the apostrophe is used incorrectly or omitted.
- Rewrite the texts correctly.

Never mind it's engine size – its the reputation of the car that matters.

Two pounds of potatoe's for the price of one.

No one is allowed to touch the horse's mouths.

Take Mr Smith and Mr Jones. Their's are the best painted houses in the street.

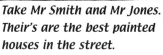

Join us to fight for womens' rights.

It does'nt take much to put your child in danger.

Your's is the only skin our product's care about.

We sha'nt take your hard-earned money. We are the worker's bank.

Dont' give your friends the chance to ask "Whose' is that old-fashioned mobile phone?"

- Write these words with the apostrophes in the correct places.
- Explain to a partner why the apostrophes go where they do.

Use a dictionary.

maam	oclock	rocknroll
Lands End	neer-do-well	will-o-the-wisp

Teachers' note When the pupils have completed the consolidation activity, spend time with them reflecting on the correct answers and why the examples here are incorrect. Stress that apostrophes should never be used in an attempt to form a plural. Draw conclusions from the examples and reinforce the rules.

Spot the difference

- Cut out the cards. Match the pairs of | homophones |.
- Match each homophone to the correct definition.
  Use a dictionary to help.

Do you think the air smells funny?

Homophones

heir	bury	course	stationery
serial	vein	faint	berry
role	kerb	vain	air
coarse	feint	principal	stationary
curb	cereal	principle	roll

Meanings

part in a play or film	belief about the way in which people should behave	the edge of a pavement where it joins the road	publication or television programme in regular instalments
rough in texture	to move by turning over and over	mixture of gases that we breathe	to put something in the ground and cover it over
lacking brightness or intensity	writing materials such as pens and paper	place where golf is played	excessively proud
person who inherits property or title	to restrain or hold back something	person in charge of a school or college	mock attack designed to distract an opponent in sport
tube in the body that carries blood	small round fruit	grain crop such as wheat or barley	not moving

Teachers' note Ask the pupils to work in pairs and give each pair a copy of this page. Pair pupils of different abilities so that they can help each other to find the words in a dictionary. First revise that homophones are words that sound the same but are spelled differently and have different meanings. Then set a time limit of five minutes for the pupils to match the cards and look up any unfamiliar words. After discussing the meanings of the words, you could ask the pupils if they can think of any more pairs of homophones.

Developing Literacy
Word Level
Year 8
© A & C BLACK

Spot the difference

- Use a dictionary to help you find a **homophone** for each of these words.
- Write sentences containing the words to show you know what they mean.

Word	Homophone	Sentence
might	*mite*	*You might find a mite in the carpet!*
minor		
moat		
mode		
mourning		
mousse		
muscle		
naval		
neigh		
nun		
pain		
pallet		
pear		

NOW TRY THIS!

- Say the following pairs of words aloud. Circle the ones that are homophones.

Some of the pairs do not sound exactly the same.

advice	device	licence	practice
advise	devise	license	practise

Use a dictionary.

- Write which word class each word belongs to (for example, noun, adjective, verb or adverb).
- Write a rule to help you remember how to spell the words.

Teachers' note The more difficult words in the extension activity can be taught in conjunction with sentence-level work. During the plenary session, encourage the pupils to use these words in sentences to make clear the distinction between nouns and verbs. The class could also collect any examples of homophones with more than one matching word, such as *pair/pare/pear*.

Developing Literacy
Word Level
Year 8
© A & C BLACK **25**

Rearrange it

STARTER

• Find shorter words inside the word *knowledgeable.* Write them in the flashes.

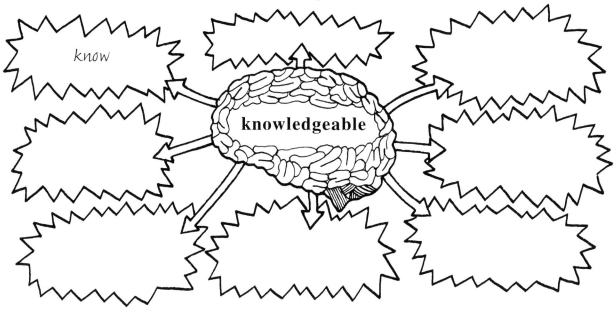

know

knowledgeable

• Now use the letters in any order to make as many new words as you can.
  Write them in the correct frames.

2-letter words

we

3-letter words

bag

4-letter words

deal

5-letter words

bleed

Words with more than 5 letters

Teachers' note Ask the pupils to work in pairs and give each pair a copy of this page. The first exercise is a good approach to finding ideas for mnemonics. After one minute, ask the pupils to share their answers. Then set a time limit of three minutes for the second exercise. The pupils will find that a large number of words can be made by using the letters in any order. Share the class's findings and discuss the longest words found. The pupils could find more words for homework.

Developing Literacy
Word Level
Year 8
© A & C BLACK

Rearrange it

• Make new words from these words. First find words within the word. Then use the letters in any order.

Check tricky spellings in a dictionary.

---

disinterested

Words inside:

interest

Letters in any order:

steer

---

thoughtlessly

Words inside:

Letters in any order:

---

international

Words inside:

Letters in any order:

---

revolutionary

Words inside:

Letters in any order:

NOW TRY THIS!

• These words can all be found in *transportation*. Write their meanings.

| notation | notion | oration |
| rotation | torsion | transit |

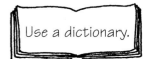
Use a dictionary.

• Find as many more words as you can in *transportation*. Give the meanings of any words that are unfamiliar to you.

Teachers' note Encourage the pupils to look up any words whose meanings are not familiar. During the plenary session, discuss the spelling and sound patterns in the words the pupils have found, paying attention to common letter strings and exceptions to spelling patterns.

Say the word

• Read the poem.

Now I surely will not *plague you*
With such words as *vague* and *ague*,
But be careful how you *speak*,
Say: *gush, bush, steak, streak, break, bleak,*
Woven, oven, how and *low,*
Script, receipt, shoe, poem, toe.
Say, expecting *fraud* and *trickery:*
Daughter, laughter and *Terpsichore,*
Branch, ranch, measles, topsails, aisles,
Missiles, similes, reviles.
Wholly, holly, signal, signing,
Same, examining, but *mining,*
Scholar, vicar, and *cigar,*
Solar, mica, war and *far.*

• Underline common ⬚ letter strings ⬚ in the words. Notice how they are pronounced.
• Complete the charts.

Words with a letter string pronounced in the same way	Words with the same letter string pronounced in a different way	Words with a letter string pronounced in the same way	Words with the same letter string pronounced in a different way
plague, vague speak,	ague		

Rhyming words which do not contain the same letter string
ague/you

Teachers' note Photocopy this page onto an OHT. Read the poem aloud to the class, paying attention to pronunciation (*ague* rhymes with *you* and *Terpsichore* rhymes with *trickery*). Then go through the poem re-reading two lines at a time, and ask the pupils to help you underline the letter strings that are the same. Write the words on the chart, grouping words which are pronounced in the same way. This can lead into a discussion about some of the irregularities of the English language, and why they have arisen.

Developing Literacy
Word Level
Year 8
© A & C BLACK

Say the word

Use a dictionary.

- All these words have a common **letter string**. Underline it in each word. How is it pronounced? _____
- Find out which language the word is derived from, and write its meaning.

Word	Language derived from	Meaning
apostrophe		
bibliophile		
catastrophe		
chlorophyll		
diaphragm		
emphatic		
haemophilia		
metaphor		
oesophagus		
pharmacy		
phenomenon		
phlegm		
physiotherapy		
physique		
sphere		

- Find three more words containing the same letter string. Complete the chart.

NOW TRY THIS!

- Say these words aloud. Write what you notice about the *h*.

| heir | honorary | hourglass | overwhelm | whale |
| whelk | whereupon | whet | whimsical | whine |

- Look at the letters which surround the *h*. Write about the pattern you notice.
- Add five more words to the list.

Teachers' note Encourage the pupils to use analogy to help them pronounce any new words. As a further extension, ask them to investigate other unusual letter strings in the words in the chart, such as *gm* in *diaphragm* and *phlegm*, and *ae* in *haemophilia*; they could think of other words containing these letter strings and research their derivations.

Developing Literacy
Word Level
Year 8
© A & C BLACK **29**

Single or double?
STARTER

- Cut out the cards.
- Match up the beginnings and endings to make new words. List the words.

dis ⟩ solve

Check your answers in a dictionary.

Beginnings	Endings
a	appear
dis	commend
dis	source
dis	cross
dis	relevant
dis	bel
dis	migrant
il	spell
il	appoint
im	ruption

Beginnings	Endings
inter	able
ir	assemble
mis	collect
mis	solve
re	literate
re	agree
re	morrow
re	legal
re	hap
to	solution

Teachers' note Split the class into small groups and give each group a copy of this page. Ask the pupils to list as many new words as they can, and to pay attention to whether the consonants are single or double. Encourage them to notice how the words are made up: for example, *morrow* is an old word for *morning*, and *to* is easily remembered. This is an example of a compound word. Word beginnings such as *dis-* and *mis-* are antonym prefixes and do not change the spelling of the root word. A double consonant occurs in *misspell* and *illegal* but no extra letters have been added.

Developing Literacy
Word Level
Year 8
© A & C BLACK

Single or double?

The gaps in the words represent either single or double letters.

- Use the letters on the notepad to complete the words.
  Write the words.

Use a dictionary to help.

su _gg_ est   *suggest*

a___lause

a___urate

co___e___pond

ques___io___aire

e___a___erate

mi___io___aire

di___a___oint

pro___e___or

ne___e___ary

pa___a___el

mi___e___ium

re___o___end

ha___a___

a___ro___

emba___a___

in___la___able

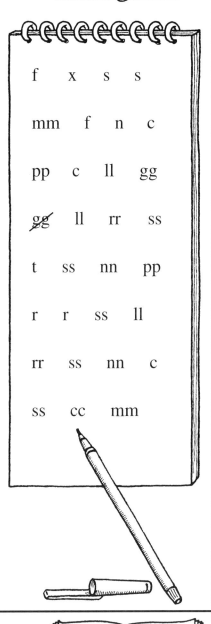

f   x   s   s

mm   f   n   c

pp   c   ll   gg

~~gg~~   ll   rr   ss

t   ss   nn   pp

r   r   ss   ll

rr   ss   nn   c

ss   cc   mm

NOW TRY THIS!

- Choose suitable **suffixes** to add to the [root words]. Decide whether or not you need to double the final consonant.

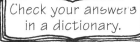
Check your answers in a dictionary.

Root words

begin	panel	enrol
open	label	common
quarrel	forget	commit
occur	happen	differ

Suffixes

-ed	-ing	-ment
-er	-al	-est
-some	-ee	-ence

Teachers' note Often there are no rules to help with these difficult words, but strategies such as splitting words into syllables or 'spell-speaking' the words may help, depending on the preferred learning styles of the individual pupils. In the extension activity there are rules to help (see page 7). See also the activity on pages 36–37.

Double act
STARTER

- Unscramble the letters to find the hidden words.

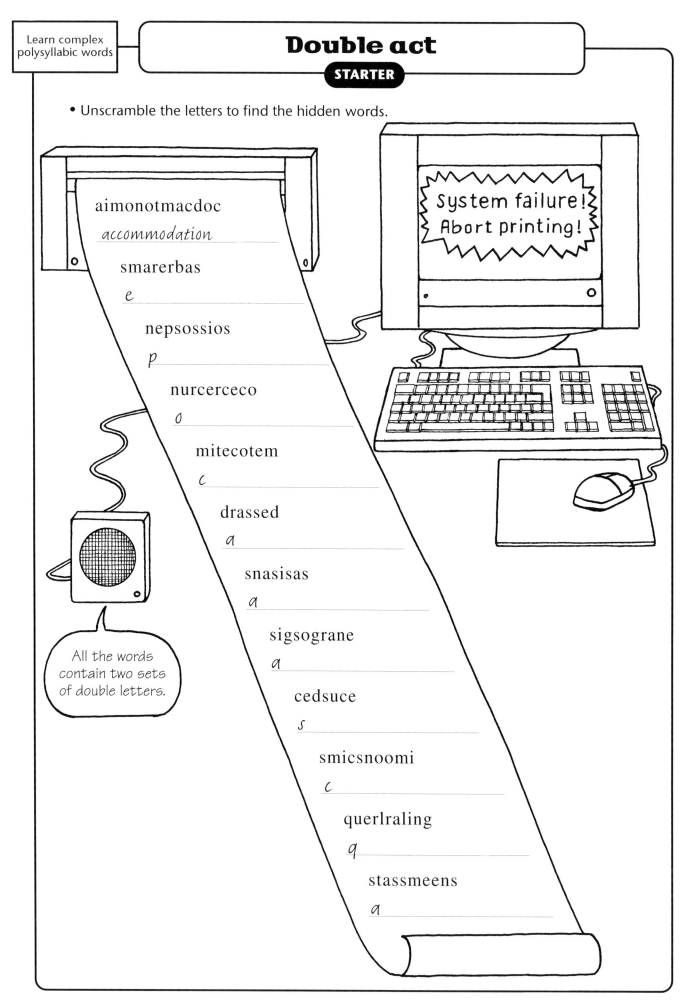

aimonotmacdoc

accommodation

smarerbas

e

nepsossios

p

nurcerceco

o

mitecotem

c

drassed

a

snasisas

a

sigsograne

a

cedsuce

s

smicsnoomi

c

querlraling

q

stassmeens

a

System failure!
Abort printing!

All the words
contain two sets
of double letters.

Teachers' note Give each pupil a copy of this page and set a time limit of five minutes for them to
find as many words as possible. Stress that it does not matter if they do not find all the words, and
ensure that they check their answers in a dictionary. Follow up the activity by discussing strategies to
help the pupils spell the words. These could include splitting the words into syllables (for example,
ad/dress, em/bar/rass) and sounding out the word in a particular rhythm (for example,
accommodation: a, double c, o, double m, o, d, a, t, i, o, n).

Developing Literacy
Word Level
Year 8
© A & C BLACK

Double act

Ten words are scrambled in the ladders.

• Join the ⊡ syllables ⊡ to make the words.

Use a ruler!

Use each syllable once.

ad	agg	ass	com	com	em	oc	pos	quar	suc

ress	mit	dress	bar	ess	mi	sess	rel	ceed	cur

tee	ion	ssion	ion	ment	rass	ring	ling

• Write the words here. Underline the pairs of double letters.

1. <u>a<u>dd</u>re<u>ss</u></u>   2. _____   3. _____   4. _____

5. _____   6. _____   7. _____   8. _____

9. _____   10. _____

• Think of ways of remembering the double letters in these words. You could try speaking the word in a special rhythm.

a, double d, r, e, double s

NOW TRY THIS!

In the **root words** below, the second syllable of the word is stressed.

• Decide whether the missing letters should be single or double. Fill in the gaps.

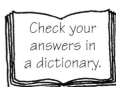

Check your answers in a dictionary.

Root word: commit

commi____ ing

commi____ ee

commi____ ment

Root word: refer

refe____ ing

refe____ ed

refe____ al

Root word: enrol

enro____ ing

enro____ ment

enro____ ed

• Think about what type of **suffix** is added each time. Write about the pattern for doubling letters in these words.

Teachers' note There are few rules to help with the spelling of these words, so the pupils will need to develop strategies. This activity offers two strategies: splitting the words into syllables and sounding words out in a particular rhythm. Note the importance of stress in the words in the extension activity (see page 7 and the activity on pages 36–37).

Developing Literacy
Word Level
Year 8
© A & C BLACK **33**

i before e?

STARTER

These words all contain *ei* or *ie*.

• Sort them according to their spellings.
  Write them on the notepads.

• Add any others you can think of.

chief

chief

protein   society   achieve   ceiling   eight   grief

conceit   either   height   foreign   brief   deceit

perceive   freight   neighbour   heir   neither   chief

die   receipt   receive   sovereign   veil

cei words

Other *ei* words

protein

ie words

Teachers' note Photocopy this page onto an OHT. Read out the words one by one and quickly sort them onto the notepads. Then ask the pupils to consider the different sounds made by the same letter combinations. Read out the *cei* words and ask whether *cei* always makes the same sound. Ask the pupils to add more words to the box and to see whether they can find any different sounds. Repeat for the *ei* words and lastly for the *ie* words. Revise the rule '*i* before *e* except after *c* whenever it rhymes with *me*'.

34

Developing Literacy
Word Level
Year 8
© A & C BLACK

i before e?

- Read the words. Decide what sounds the *ie* or *ei* letters make.
- Write the words in the correct place on the chart.

ie *ei*

~~field~~   receipt   brief   their   weird   siege   conceive
medieval   height   achieve   tie   reign   niece   deceit   vein
mischief   pie   quiet   piece   receive   heir   pier   seize
weigh   priest   shield   lie   shriek   ceiling   neighbour   believe

Sounds like *ee* in *feet*		Sounds like *ay* in *pay*	
ie words	*ei* words	*ie* words	*ei* words
field			

Sounds like *air* in *hair*	
ie words	*ei* words

Sounds like *i* in *mile*	
ie words	*ei* words

- Write about the spelling patterns for each different sound.

Long a sounds like 'ay' in 'pay' are spelled...

NOW TRY THIS!

- Which of these words do not follow the sound and spelling patterns you have described? Underline them.

fiend	friend	patient	perceiving	protein	relief
review	seize	sieve	species	spies	weird

- Think of ways you can remember how to spell these words.
  Example: *There is prot**ei**n **in** eggs.*

Teachers' note The pupils will find that there are many exceptions to the '*i* before *e*' rule. Draw out the rules and exceptions during the plenary session. The extension activity encourages the pupils to find strategies such as mnemonics to help them remember how to spell the exceptions. It will be helpful to discuss different types of mnemonics, such as those on pages 48–49.

Stressed out!

STARTER

- Read these words aloud. Split them into **syllables**.
- Decide which syllable is stressed when you say the word. Underline it.

Word	Syllable 1	Syllable 2
alter		
begin		
commit		
forget		
limit		
market		

al/ter

- Choose | vowel suffixes | to add to the words on the chart. Write the new words.

Vowel suffixes
-ing   -ed
    -able

alter +ing

Word	New words with vowel suffixes
alter	
begin	
commit	
forget	
limit	
market	

- How many syllables does each word contain? _____

- If the stress is on the first syllable, what happens to the final consonant when you

  add a vowel suffix? _____

- If the stress is on the second syllable, what happens to the final consonant when you

  add a vowel suffix? _____

- Find other examples to test your rules.

Teachers' note Photocopy this page onto an OHT. Before beginning, briefly revise the doubling of letters when adding suffixes to words of one syllable (see page 7). Explain that in words of more than one syllable, where the stress (or emphasis) falls can affect whether or not the final consonant doubles. With the class, split the words into syllables and then decide which is stressed. After completing the charts, answer the questions together. Remind the pupils that these are vowel suffixes only, and that consonant suffixes do not follow the same pattern.

Developing Literacy
Word Level
Year 8
© A & C BLACK

Stressed out!

When you add a **suffix** to words of more than one syllable, you need to decide whether to double the last letter of the word. Knowing where the stress falls in the word can help you to decide.

The stress is on the syllable that you emphasise when you say the word.

- Choose **vowel suffixes** and consonant suffixes to add to these words. Check your new words in a dictionary.

Vowel suffixes

-ing   -ed   -er

Consonant suffixes

-ment   -ful

admit   or   admit?

Word	Stress on first or second syllable?	New words with vowel suffixes	New words with consonant suffixes
admit	*second*	*admitting, admitted*	–
begin			
commit			
enrol			
fidget			
occur			
offer			
prefer			
profit			
refer			
regret			
visit			

- Write a rule about when to double the final letters of words with more than one syllable.

_____

_____

_____

NOW TRY THIS!

- Test your rule by adding vowel suffixes to these words.

| fulfil | handicap | kidnap | label |
| propel | rival | travel | worship |

Check your answers in a dictionary.

- What do you notice about these words?

Teachers' note First revise the difference between vowel suffixes and consonant suffixes. It may be useful to practise sounding out the words and finding where the stress comes. Try exaggerating the sounds to make the point; the natural stress becomes obvious when this is done. During the plenary session, discuss the rules and the exceptions that the pupils have discovered (see page 7).

-ible or -able?

STARTER

- Cut out the word cards. Sort them into words ending in *-ible* and words ending in *-able*.
- Circle all the **suffixes** (*-ible* and *-able*). Underline the part of the word that is left. What difference do you notice between *-ible* and *-able* words?
- Brainstorm other *-ible* and *-able* words to test your theory.

Be careful – there are exceptions!

breakable	audible
bendable	washable
permissible	visible
adaptable	legible
agreeable	presentable
compatible	comfortable
edible	countable
laughable	avoidable
horrible	plausible

Teachers' note Ask the pupils to work in pairs and give each pair a copy of this page. Set a time limit of five minutes for the pupils to sort the cards and look for the patterns in the word roots. Bring together their findings and invite them to share the new examples they have thought of. There are many exceptions to the rule, some of which are investigated in the consolidation activity. Encourage the pupils to look up the meanings of any unfamiliar words.

Developing Literacy
Word Level
Year 8
© A & C BLACK

-ible or -able?

- Add *-ible* or *-able* to the following. Write the new words.

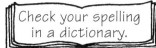
Check your spelling in a dictionary.

accept   ⟶   *acceptable*

access   ⟶

comprehens ⟶

convert   ⟶

divis   ⟶

fashion   ⟶

favour   ⟶

incred   ⟶

invis   ⟶

perish   ⟶

poss   ⟶

prefer   ⟶

terr   ⟶

understand ⟶

- Circle all the **suffixes** (*-ible* and *-able*). Look at the part of the word that is left.
- Write a rule for types of word that end in *-ible* and those that end in *-able*.
- List as many exceptions to the rule as you can find.

Exceptions

- Add the suffix *-ible* or *-able* to these words. Write the new words.

envy

justify   ⟶   **+ *-ible* or *-able***

rely

- Explain how the spelling changes when you add *-ible* or *-able* to words ending in *y*.

- Add the suffix *-ible* or *-able* to these words. Write the new words.

| admire | debate | desire | forgive | inflate |
| love | manage | measure | notice | remove |

Check your spelling in a dictionary.

- Explain what happens to most words ending in *e* when you add *-ible* or *-able*.
- Explain why some words are exceptions to the rule.

Teachers' note Stress that there are exceptions to the rule. Many of these follow other rules with which the pupils will be familiar (such as *y* changing to *i* in *rely – reliable* and dropping the final *e* in *admire – admirable*). During the plenary session, discuss why words such as *manageable* and *noticeable* retain the final *e* (to avoid making a hard *g* or *c* sound).

Should 'e' stay?
STARTER

- Investigate what happens to these words when you drop the final *e*. Write the new words.

How does the vowel sound change? **!**

cube ⟶ *cub*   gape ⟶ _____   hate ⟶ _____

made ⟶ _____   mate ⟶ _____   pipe ⟶ _____

ripe ⟶ _____   slime ⟶ _____   wine ⟶ _____

- Investigate what happens when you add **vowel suffixes** to the words below. Write the words.

Vowel suffixes
-ing   -ation   -able

admire ⟶ _____   change ⟶ _____

cure ⟶ _____   define ⟶ _____

desire ⟶ _____   dine ⟶ _____

organise ⟶ _____   prepare ⟶ _____

separate ⟶ _____   shine ⟶ _____

- Investigate what happens when you add **consonant suffixes** to the words below. Write the words.

Consonant suffixes
-ly   -ful   -ment

advertise ⟶ _____   approximate ⟶ _____

arrange ⟶ _____   fortunate ⟶ _____

lone ⟶ _____   scarce ⟶ _____

severe ⟶ _____   spite ⟶ _____

strange ⟶ _____   use ⟶ _____

Teachers' note Photocopy this page onto an OHT. First revise short and long vowel sounds: long vowels 'say their name in the alphabet' (for example, *a* in *pay* and *o* in *cone*). Complete the first exercise with the pupils and discuss that the long vowel sounds become short when the *e* is removed. The second and third exercises show that the final *e* is dropped when a vowel suffix is added but not when a consonant suffix is added (the consolidation activity looks at exceptions). Encourage the pupils to use other vowel and consonant suffixes in addition to those on the page.

Developing Literacy
Word Level
Year 8
© A & C BLACK

Should 'e' stay?

• Add **vowel suffixes** and **consonant suffixes** to these words. Check your answers in a dictionary.

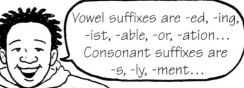

Vowel suffixes are -ed, -ing, -ist, -able, -or, -ation... Consonant suffixes are -s, -ly, -ment...

Word	New words with vowel suffixes	New words with consonant suffixes
agitate	*agitated, agitating, agitator*	*agitates*
behave		
compete		
conceive		
continue		
excite		
guide		
prepare		
separate		
suppose		
time		

• Write a rule about adding suffixes to words ending in *e*.

_____

_____

• Write the meanings of these words. Discuss with a partner why you think some of the words keep the final *e* of the **root word**.

singeing _____   singing _____

dyeing _____   dying _____

swingeing _____   swinging _____

• Discuss with a partner why you think these words keep the final *e* of the root word.

| hoeing   shoeing   eyeing   ageing |

NOW TRY THIS!

• List exceptions to the rule about adding consonant suffixes.
  Examples: *truly, argument*
• List words which keep the final *e* in order to keep a *c* or *g* sounding soft.
  Examples: *outrageous, noticeable*

Teachers' note For the extension activity, the pupils could look in texts they are studying or refer to previous work on these spelling rules. During the plenary session, discuss the reasons why certain words retain the final *e* of the root word with a vowel suffix (see page 8).

Developing Literacy
Word Level
Year 8
© A & C BLACK **41**

Book of words

STARTER

- Cut out the cards. Put the entries from an etymological dictionary in alphabetical order.
- Find out which are true ⌈ derivations ⌋ of the words.
- If any are false, find the true derivations and write them down.

umpire

From a Russian word, meaning someone who applies a law or rule. The original word was *numpire*, but this gradually changed to 'an umpire'.

escape

From Latin, meaning 'out of cape'. Ancient Romans felt released from constraint when they took off their capes, and so 'escape' came to mean gaining freedom.

witness

From the ancient German term *witan*, which described wise tribal elders who followed the Norse god Woden (or Odin) and were present at every ceremony of worship.

denim

This cloth was originally made in Nîmes, France. It was called *serge de Nîmes* and was later shortened to *de Nîmes* (denim).

slogan

From a Gaelic word meaning 'war-cry', used by Scottish Highlanders. It was formed from the Gaelic words for 'army' and 'shout'. The present meaning 'catchphrase' came about in the eighteenth century.

scout

A scout was originally someone who sneaked around silently. The word comes from the Latin word *auscultare*, meaning 'to creep'. The ancient Romans used this word to describe enemy spies.

suede

From *gants de Suède,* French for 'gloves from Sweden'. The soft leather now called suede was first made in Sweden and the French brought the suede gloves to mainland Europe.

tennis

The sport first developed in France and was originally called *tenez*, from the French verb *tenir*. Players used to say this word as they hit the ball to one another. It meant 'there you go'.

Teachers' note Split the class into groups and give each group a copy of this page. The pupils should cut out the cards and distribute them among the members of the group. Ensure that dictionaries (preferably etymological ones) are readily available; ICT resources can also be used. After allowing time for the pupils to investigate the words, draw together their findings and ask for the true derivations. End the session by discussing how the derivation of a word can help with spelling.

Developing Literacy
Word Level
Year 8
© A & C BLACK

Book of words

• Write these words associated with art in alphabetical order.

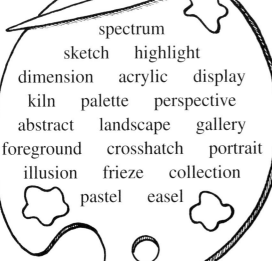

spectrum
sketch   highlight
dimension   acrylic   display
kiln   palette   perspective
abstract   landscape   gallery
foreground   crosshatch   portrait
illusion   frieze   collection
pastel   easel

'Fanatic' and 'figure' are the first and last words on a dictionary page.

• Underline the words you would find on that page.

• Write them on the page in alphabetical order.

figment   file   fang

farce   fellow   femur

fan   fair   farther

favour   felon   feminine

fever   fibula   fiction

fillet   famish   feign

feature   fascinate   festoon

filial   fawn   February

fervent   fiery

fanatic		
		figure

NOW TRY THIS!

• Match each word in box **A** with a | synonym | in box **B**. Write out the pairs of words. Use a dictionary to help.

Synonyms are words with the same meaning.   **!**

A

hate   house   disaster
greedy   lazy   busy
waste   pierce   stubborn

B

catastrophe   indolent   extravagance
animosity   penetrate   industrious
avaricious   obstinate   abode

Teachers' note Before beginning, revise the quartiles of a dictionary and stress the importance of using the 'header words' at the top of each page in order to find one's way around the reference source quickly and efficiently. Encourage the pupils to look up any words on the page whose meanings they do not know. A thesaurus could be used for the extension activity.

The same but different
STARTER

• Write words containing these **letter strings**.

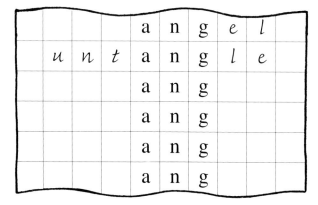

What's the longest word you can find?

			a	n	g	*e*	*l*	
u	*n*	*t*	a	n	g	*l*	*e*	
			a	n	g			
			a	n	g			
			a	n	g			
			a	n	g			

	e	a	d	
	e	a	d	
	e	a	d	
	e	a	d	
	e	a	d	
	e	a	d	

	i	n	t	
	i	n	t	
	i	n	t	
	i	n	t	
	i	n	t	
	i	n	t	

	a	g	e	
	a	g	e	
	a	g	e	
	a	g	e	
	a	g	e	
	a	g	e	

	a	n	d	
	a	n	d	
	a	n	d	
	a	n	d	
	a	n	d	
	a	n	d	

	i	n	g	
	i	n	g	
	i	n	g	
	i	n	g	
	i	n	g	
	i	n	g	

	o	u	g	h	
	o	u	g	h	
	o	u	g	h	
	o	u	g	h	
	o	u	g	h	
	o	u	g	h	

	o	u	r	
	o	u	r	
	o	u	r	
	o	u	r	
	o	u	r	
	o	u	r	

Teachers' note Photocopy this page onto an OHT. Focus on one letter string at a time and write the words in the grids as the pupils think of them. Encourage them to think of long words, and to consider the different sounds made by the letter string in different words. When the grids have been completed, discuss how many different sounds are created by each letter string. Ask whether the letters surrounding the letter string affect the way in which it is pronounced.

Developing Literacy
Word Level
Year 8
© A & C BLACK

44

- Read aloud the word in the speech bubble. Write three words containing the same │ vowel phoneme │, spelled in the same way.

- Beneath, write a word that sounds different but contains the same **letter string**.

A phoneme is the smallest unit of sound in a word.

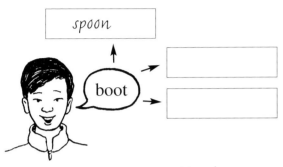

spoon

boot

Different sound: _blood_

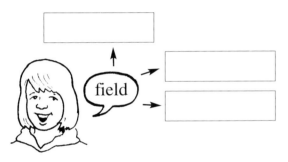

field

Different sound: _____

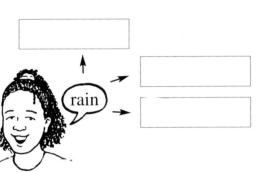

rain

Different sound: _____

meat

Different sound: _____

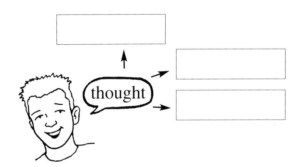

thought

Different sound: _____

shout

Different sound: _____

NOW TRY THIS!

- List as many words as you can containing the letter string *augh*. Group them according to the way the letter string is pronounced.

- Write how many **phonemes** the letter string *augh* makes in each word.

- Make up a silly sentence containing the words to help you remember that they all contain *augh*.

daughter, haughty, draughty...

Teachers' note Before beginning, revise phonemes and practise with the pupils sounding out a variety of long and short vowel phonemes. Revise that a long vowel 'says its name in the alphabet' (for example, *a* in *pay* and *o* in *cone*). It is useful to remind pupils that English is not a regular language and that for most rules there are exceptions.

Syllable splits
STARTER

- Choose words from the list. Write them on the strips on the right, with a **syllable** in each section.
- Cut out the strips. Then cut out the card at the bottom of the page and cut along the dashes.
- Thread the strips through the slits in an under-and-over pattern.
- Pull the strips to match up syllables and make new words. List all the words you make.

Check your words in a dictionary.

per	spect	ive

perspective   intending   mineral
percussion   designing   dissolving
intention   employment   prevention
admission   processor   obtaining
reducing   important   generous
mistaken   narrative   remember
digestion   contorted   editor

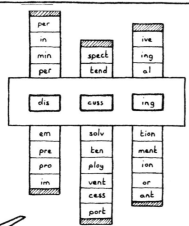

Teachers' note Ask the pupils to work in pairs and give each pair a copy of this page. First revise splitting words into syllables, and the difference between a syllable and a phoneme (each syllable must contain a vowel or a *y*). Discuss that there are different ways of splitting words into syllables. The activity will work best if the pupils take prefixes and suffixes as syllables (for example, *dis/solv/ing*). Once the pupils have made the 'sliders', set a time limit of three minutes for them to make as many new words as possible and list them.

Developing Literacy
Word Level
Year 8
© A & C BLACK

46

Syllable splits

- Divide these maths words into **syllables**.
- Write the complete words again.

Remember, each syllable must contain a vowel or a 'y'.

Word	Syllables					Write the word
	1	2	3	4	5	
addition	add	i	tion			addition
approximately						
circumference						
corresponding						
denominator						
division						
equation						
equilateral						
horizontal						
irregular						
isosceles						
multiplication						
parallelogram						
percentage						
perimeter						
perpendicular						
quadrilateral						
subtraction						
symmetrical						
triangular						

NOW TRY THIS!

- Think of other strategies for remembering how to spell the words. You could try these methods.

Find a word within the word: equi<u>late</u>ral

Write or draw **a mnemonic**: My <u>mate</u> is approxi<u>mate</u>ly five foot eight.

Investigate the **derivation** of root words, prefixes and suffixes: ir- regular

Use the Look, Say, Cover, Write and Check strategy.

Teachers' note Encourage the pupils to tap out the syllable sounds of words and to say them aloud if they find the exercise difficult. For the extension activity, it may be useful briefly to revise the methods outlined. During the plenary, stress that spelling strategies are often very personal; what works for one pupil may not work for another because everyone learns in different ways.

Developing Literacy
Word Level
Year 8
© A & C BLACK **47**

Memory test

STARTER

1. Silly sentences can help you to remember words that share the same **letter strings**.

> Ghastly ghoulish ghosts
> live in draughty troughs.

• Make up silly sentences to help you remember the letter strings in these words.

lodger	ledge
fudge	edge

_____

_____

switched	blotchy
snatched	watch

_____

_____

2. Discuss how these 'word drawings' are useful for remembering the spellings of the words.

CAL END A R   U-t U rn   palm   EMBA RR ASS

3. You can memorise the shape of the written word. In these words, notice which letters have ⬚ ascenders ⬚ (tall letters like *h*, *b* and *k*) and which have ⬚ descenders ⬚ (like *g* and *y*).

myth rhyme justify

4. Written **mnemonics** can also help with tricky parts of words.

> I shall be your fri**end** until the **end**.

• Make up mnemonics for these words.

piece	**great**	**bus**iness	build

Teachers' note Photocopy this page onto an OHT. Explain that if the pupils find any word or group of words difficult, they can look for the problem areas of the words and find ways to memorise them. Go through the strategies on the OHT to discover which are the most useful. Stress that whatever works for each pupil is valid; there is no one correct approach. Invite the pupils to make up their own examples. When identifying common letter strings, point out the need to remember words that do **not** follow the pattern, such as *lodger/edge/privilege* and *switch/watch/attach*.

Developing Literacy
Word Level
Year 8
© A & C BLACK

Memory test

• Find ways of remembering the difficult parts of these science words. Use whichever method you find easiest.

You could:
• make up a silly sentence
• make up a 'word drawing'
• draw the shape of the word
• write a **mnemonic** using the chart below.

cycle

mammal	nutrient

organism	oxygen

predator	pressure

temperature	vertebrate

• Use this chart to help you write mnemonics. You could look for a word within the word as a starting idea.

Word	Words inside	Mnemonic

NOW TRY THIS!

• Think of drawings or written mnemonics to help you remember how to spell these RE words. Use their shapes, sounds or letter patterns.

Buddhist	celebration	Christian	disciple
Islam	marriage	pilgrimage	synagogue

Teachers' note The pupils will find it helpful to refer to the examples on the starter OHT. During the plenary session, discuss which strategies the pupils found the most helpful.

Transform it

STARTER

- Change one letter at a time to make new words. Try to get from the start word to the finish word in the correct number of steps.

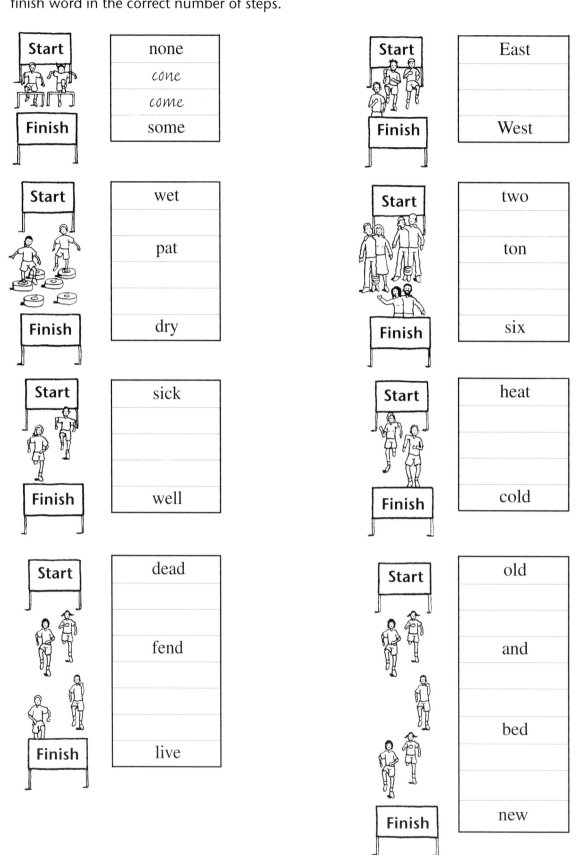

Start

| none |
| *cone* |
| *come* |
| some |

Finish

Start

| East |
| |
| West |

Finish

Start

| wet |
| |
| pat |
| |
| dry |

Finish

Start

| two |
| |
| ton |
| |
| six |

Finish

Start

| sick |
| |
| |
| |
| well |

Finish

Start

| heat |
| |
| |
| |
| cold |

Finish

Start

| dead |
| |
| fend |
| |
| |
| live |

Finish

Start

| old |
| |
| and |
| |
| bed |
| |
| |
| new |

Finish

Teachers' note Organise the pupils into small mixed-ability groups and give each group a copy of this page. Model the first example with the class and explain the strategy; they should decide which letters they want to keep the same and which they want to change. Then they should try changing one letter at a time to make a new word. Make sure that an alphabet is in view and encourage the pupils to look up new words in a dictionary if they are unsure. The activity can be done as a race. **50** Some of the puzzles are challenging, so do not expect all groups to complete the activity.

Developing Literacy
Word Level
Year 8
© A & C BLACK

Transform it

• Rearrange the letters to make a new word from each ⬚anagram⬚ .

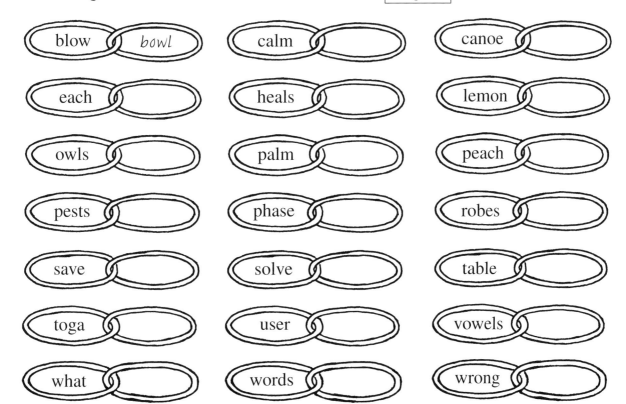

blow — *bowl* calm canoe

each heals lemon

owls palm peach

pests phase robes

save solve table

toga user vowels

what words wrong

• Make two new words from each of these anagrams.

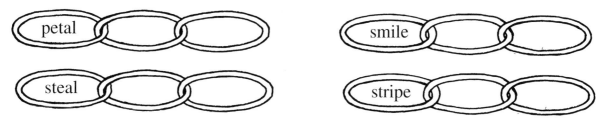

petal smile

steal stripe

• Think of three words of your own which can be used as anagrams. Write the word pairs.

NOW TRY THIS!

• Insert a letter into each word to make a new word.

Try putting the letter within the word, not at the beginning or end. **!**

| beach | dying | fight | gasp | hoping |
| led | sowing | steam | step | tough |

Example: *beach* ⟶ *bleach*

Teachers' note If the pupils find solving the anagrams difficult, suggest that they write the letters of the anagram in a circle in a random order and then see if they can see any other word forming. For the extension activity, encourage them to notice how inserting a single letter can affect the vowel sounds.

Speak Anglo-Saxon!

STARTER

Anglo-Saxon language is all around us – we just don't realise it!

- Look at this chart from an etymological dictionary.

Anglo-Saxon word	Meaning	Recognise it as...
bearu	grove, wood	barrow
beorg	hill, burial-mound	borough, burgh
brycg	bridge	brig, bridge, brid
burh	fortified place	bur, borough, burgh, bury
burna	stream, spring	bourne, burn, borne
cot	shelter, cottage	coat, cote, cot
dun	hill, down	dun, down, don, ton
ham	homestead, village	ham
ing	place of, group of people	ing
leah	glade, clearing	leigh, lee, ley, le
mere	lake, pool	mer, mar, mere
stan	stone	stan, ston, stone
stede	place, site	sted, stead
tun	enclosure, village	ton, town
wich	group of houses	wich, wick

Stanstead – site of the stone

Burnley – stream in a clearing

- List place names which are derived from Anglo-Saxon.
- Write what you think the place names mean.

Use an atlas or a map of your local area.

Place name	Parts derived from Anglo-Saxon	Meaning of place name
Birmingham	ing, ham	village of the people of Birm

Teachers' note Photocopy this page onto an OHT. For this activity the pupils will need an atlas or a map of your local area. First explain that the English language has developed from many sources, and one of these is Anglo-Saxon. Read the chart with the class and discuss the examples of place names on the sheet. Then ask the pupils to suggest other place names which they think are derived from Anglo-Saxon, using maps and atlases to help. Invite them to complete the chart.

Developing Literacy
Word Level
Year 8
© A & C BLACK

Speak Anglo-Saxon!

• Say these Anglo-Saxon words aloud. Write them as we would today.

Anglo-Saxon word	Modern spelling
boc	*book*
brun	
grene	
mete	
milc	
modor	
waeter	

You still use these Anglo-Saxon words today.

The **prefixes** and **suffixes** on the chart below come from Anglo-Saxon.

• Decide whether each is a prefix or a suffix. Write examples of words containing it. Write what you think the prefix or suffix means.

	Prefix or suffix?	Words containing it	Meaning of prefix or suffix
craft	*suffix*	*witchcraft, needlecraft*	*skill or strength*
dom			
est			
for			
less			
mis			
un			

• Find a modern word that you think is derived from each Anglo-Saxon word.

beatan (to hit or strike) _____   witan (to know) _____

beran (to carry) _____

• Write the modern equivalents of these Anglo-Saxon words. The clues will help you.

abbod   biscop

cirice   flocc

godsibb   hund

hus   twa

werold   wivan

Clues: jobs in the church

tittle-tattle

_____ heads are better than one

old _____' tales

the _____'s your oyster

_____ of Commons

Horse and _____

holy building

While shepherds watched their…

Teachers' note Encourage the pupils to read the Anglo-Saxon words phonetically, using hard sounds rather than soft ones. They will need access to good dictionaries in order to find information about the prefixes and suffixes. Use the plenary session to discuss what has been discovered and to consider the impact of this ancient language on how we spell today.

That's a new one!

STARTER

- Cut out the cards. Write on each card what the word means and how it was created.

---

e-commerce

Meaning: _____

_____

How created: _____

emoticon

Meaning: _____

_____

How created: _____

---

guerrilla

Meaning: _____

_____

How created: _____

helicopter

Meaning: _____

_____

How created: _____

---

hydrofoil

Meaning: _____

_____

How created: _____

microwave

Meaning: _____

_____

How created: _____

---

motel

Meaning: _____

_____

How created: _____

netiquette

Meaning: _____

_____

How created: _____

---

polyester

Meaning: _____

_____

How created: _____

radar

Meaning: _____

_____

How created: _____

---

supermarket

Meaning: _____

_____

How created: _____

telesales

Meaning: _____

_____

How created: _____

Teachers' note Ask the pupils to work in groups of four to six, and give each group a copy of this page. First explain that English is a constantly evolving language and still adopts new words to describe new ideas or processes. Explain that the words on the sheet were all new words to the twentieth century. Ask the pupils to share out the cards and to use dictionaries and the Internet to research the derivations of the words. They should be aware that if words are very new they may not be recorded in printed dictionaries. Invite them to share their findings at the end of the session.

Developing Literacy
Word Level
Year 8
© A & C BLACK

That's a new one!

These words have all acquired new meanings in the past 100 years.

- Explain the new meaning and the original, older meaning.
- List all the different meanings you can think of.

It's a virus...

virus

New meaning(s):   Old meaning(s):

park

New meaning(s):   Old meaning(s):

wing

New meaning(s):   Old meaning(s):

rock

New meaning(s):   Old meaning(s):

surf

New meaning(s):   Old meaning(s):

NOW TRY THIS!

Many words have old meanings that are rarely used today, if at all.

- Find out the **derivations** of these words, and their old and new meanings.

| naughty | wicked | villain | meat | humour | vulgar |

Example: *naughty*   *Derivation: from the word 'naught' (nothing)*
Used to mean: worth nothing
Now means: badly behaved

Teachers' note When the pupils have written down all the meanings they can think of, they should look up the words in a dictionary to ensure that they understand all the meanings. During the plenary session, discuss how the meanings of words can change over time.

Rhyme and reason

STARTER

Use your loaf!

Cockney rhyming slang uses rhyming phrases in the place of everyday words.

- Cut out the cards. Pick a card and say what you think the phrase means.

bacon and eggs 	plates of meat 
frog and toad	mince pies 
north and south	skin and blister 
bread and honey 	tea leaf
whistle and flute 	baked bean
Adam and Eve	jam jar
currant bun	butcher's hook
holy friar	trouble and strife
tomfoolery	china plate
dog and bone	bricks and mortar 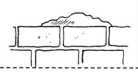

Teachers' note Ask the pupils to work in groups of about six, and give each group a copy of this page. First introduce cockney rhyming slang and explain, with examples, that the last word of the phrase rhymes with the word it represents. The pupils should take turns to pick a card and read out the phrase; as a group they should discuss and write down what they think it means. All the words are nouns or verbs. Stress that it does not matter if the pupils' ideas are not correct. At the end of the session, discuss their ideas and review the answers (see page 9).

Developing Literacy
Word Level
Year 8
© A & C BLACK

Rhyme and reason

Use analogy to improve spelling

- Add *s* or *ss* followed by *ion* to make nouns.

	+ s or ss	+ ion	Write the noun
conclu	*s*	*ion*	*conclusion*
discu			
progre			
divi			
confe			
permi			
ero			
diver			

Check your answers in a dictionary.

- Complete the chart below to show the spelling patterns.

Noun	Root word (verb)	Does noun contain complete root word?		Root word final vowel sound		Root word final consonant	
		Yes	No	Long	Short	Single	Double
conclusion	*conclude*		✔	✔		✔	

- Write a rule about words ending in *-sion* and those ending in *-ssion*. Note any exceptions.

NOW TRY THIS!

- Draw a chart and sort these *ough* words according to the sounds they make.
- Write **mnemonics** to help you spell *ough* words that you find difficult.

| plough | although | bought | cough | tough | fought | enough | ought |
| bough | drought | borough | through | rough | thought | thorough | trough |

Sounds like *o* in *bone*	Sounds like *off*	Sounds like...	Sounds like...

Teachers' note Before beginning, revise that root words are words to which prefixes and suffixes can be added: for example, *discuss – discussion* (root word is *discuss*). For the extension activity, it may be useful briefly to revise different types of mnemonics (see pages 48–49 and 58).

Troublesome words
STARTER

- Cut out the cards. Choose three cards each.
- Circle the parts of the words that are difficult to spell. Then work out strategies for learning to spell the words. You could try these methods.

Split the word into **phonemes**: rh/y/me or **syllables**: se/par/ate	Find a word within the word: con(science)	Make up **mnemonics**. *The chemist and the chiropodist sing chords in the Christian choir.* 
Investigate the **derivation** of root words, prefixes and suffixes: mis -lead	Use the Look, Say, Cover, Write and Check strategy.	

analysis	beautiful	criticism
decision	descendant	disappoint
guarantee	indispensable	miscellaneous
necessary	opportunity	permanent
prejudice	privilege	secretary

Teachers' note Split the class into groups of five and give each group a copy of this page. Before beginning, talk through each of the strategies outlined to show how they can help. Encourage the pupils to share their strategies with the group, and to find other 'difficult' words that will reinforce the strategies (for example, *guarantee* shares the *gu* letter string with *guest, league* and *ghost*). All the pupils will have something worthwhile to bring to this activity.

Developing Literacy
Word Level
Year 8
© A & C BLACK

Troublesome words

- List words that you find difficult to spell.

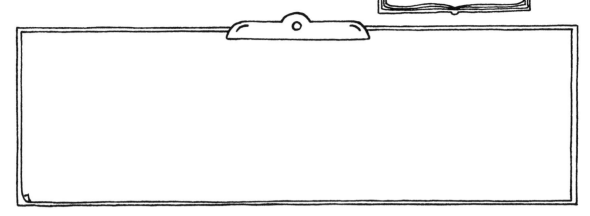

Use a dictionary.

- Complete the charts to help you remember how to spell the words.

Strategy 1

- Look for **root words**, **prefixes** or **suffixes** in the words. Make notes about their **derivation**.
- List other words in the same **word family**.

Word	Root word	Prefix	Suffix	Notes on derivation	Words in same family
disappoint	appoint	dis	–	dis – prefix appoint – from French	appointment reappoint

Strategy 2

- Look for a word within the word.

Word	Words inside		Word	Words inside
privilege	vile, leg			

Teachers' note The pupils can use this sheet as a spelling log to record words they find difficult. They could file several copies of the sheet and add to them throughout the year. Explain that the strategies may be useful for only some of the words; the pupils will need to decide which strategy works best for each word. See also page 63.

Developing Literacy
Word Level
Year 8
© A & C BLACK **59**

Unfamiliar words

STARTER

1. Make words related to ICT by combining words or **prefixes** from computer **A** with words from computer **B**.

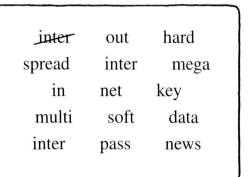

Computer A:
inter	out	hard
spread	inter	mega
in	net	key
multi	soft	data
inter	pass	news

Computer B:
put	byte	net
group	board	put
ware	media	work
ware	word	active
sheet	base	face

New words

interface

_____

2. Vowels can sometimes be difficult to make out because they are spoken quickly or quietly. These are called unstressed vowels .

• Circle the unstressed vowels in these ICT words.

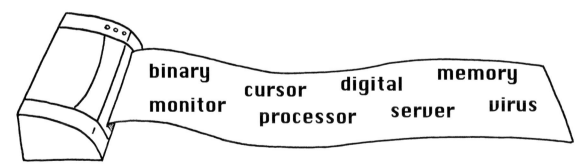

binary **cursor** **digital** **memory** **monitor** **processor** **server** **virus**

• Practise saying the words with exaggerated pronunciation to help you remember the unstressed vowels.

Teachers' note Photocopy this page onto an OHT. Invite the pupils to make ICT words using each of the word components once; write their new words on the OHT. Discuss that some are compound words and others are formed from a prefix and a root word. Recognising the ways in which words are made up will help the pupils with spelling. In the second exercise, invite them to say the words and to identify the unstressed vowels. Model how to exaggerate the pronunciation (for example, *curs-OR*).

Developing Literacy
Word Level
Year 8
© A & C BLACK

Unfamiliar words

- List any unfamiliar words you have come across in your work in other subjects. Use this page to help you learn to spell them.

Unfamiliar words which are difficult to spell	Which part of the word is difficult?	Other words you know with a similar spelling problem
aesthetic	silent 'a'	archaeology, paediatric

- Choose a strategy for each word. Write the words on the appropriate parts of this chart. Write or draw your strategies on the chart, or on another piece of paper.

Strategy 1: Split the word into **phonemes** or **syllables**.	**Strategy 2:** Exaggerate the pronunciation of the word.	**Strategy 3:** Find a word within the word.
Strategy 4: Make up **mnemonics** such as word drawings or silly sentences.	**Strategy 5:** Investigate the **derivation** of root words, prefixes and suffixes.	**Strategy 6:** Use the Look, Say, Cover, Write and Check strategy.

Teachers' note Use this sheet in conjunction with work in other subjects. The sheet provides a useful resource for the pupils to record their difficulties and to think of strategies to help spell the words. Stress that everyone learns in different ways and that there is no one correct approach: whatever strategy works for the individual is valid.

On the subject

STARTER

- Cut out the cards. Pick out all the words you would use in history.
- Look up any words whose meaning you do not know.
- On the blank cards, write other history words that you find difficult to spell.

Use a dictionary.

disease	bias	alkaline
religious	document	Protestant
cathedral	imperialism	Catholic
citizen	source	contour
propaganda	anthology	defence
immigrant	parliament	dynasty
medieval	polyester	emigration
constitutional	agriculture	contradict
personification	government	independence
isosceles	civilisation	processor
colony	rebel	siege
percussion	invasion	chronology

Teachers' note Split the class into small groups and give each group a copy of this page. Encourage the pupils to write definitions of words whose meanings they do not know (this could be done within a time limit of three minutes). At the end of the session, discuss the meanings of the history words and what parts of the words make them difficult to spell. Invite the pupils to share the other history words they have listed. These words can then be used with the consolidation activity.

Developing Literacy
Word Level
Year 8
© A & C BLACK

On the subject

Subject: _____

• List words in this subject that you find difficult to spell.

• Complete the charts to help you remember how to spell the words.

Strategy 1

• Split the words into **syllables**. Practise saying the words, pronouncing each part clearly.

con/sti/tu/tion/al

Word	Syllable 1	Syllable 2	Syllable 3	Syllable 4	Syllable 5
constitutional	con	sti	tu	tion	al

Strategy 2

• Make up **mnemonics** to help you spell the tricky parts of the words.

Word	Mnemonic
medieval	People would <u>die</u> young in med<u>ie</u>val times.

Strategy 3

• Use the Look, Say, Cover, Write and Check strategy.

Teachers' note The pupils could file several copies of this sheet and add to them throughout the year. Explain that some strategies may be useful for only some of the words; the pupils will need to decide which strategy works best for each word. Discuss that there are several ways of splitting words into syllables (for example, _con/sti/tu/tion/al, cons/ti/tu/tio/nal_). See also page 59.

Developing Literacy
Word Level
Year 8
© A & C BLACK **63**

Glossary

adjective A word that describes a noun: for example, *blue, round, tall*.

adverb A word that gives information about a verb. It says how something happens: for example, *she shouted loudly; the bus stopped suddenly*.

anagram A word or phrase whose letters can be rearranged to make a different word or phrase: for example, *step/pest*.

analogy Recognising a sound or letter pattern in known words and applying this to new, unfamiliar words.

antonym prefix A prefix that can be added to a word to form a word with the opposite meaning: for example, *un- (un- + tie = untie); mis- (mis- + behave = misbehave)*.

ascender The part of a letter (such as *h* or *k*) that extends above the body of the letter.

compound word A word made up from other complete words: for example, *black + berry = blackberry*.

consonant suffix A suffix that begins with a consonant: for example, *-ly, -ment, -ful, -s*.

contraction A shortened form in which an apostrophe replaces omitted letters: for example, *you're (you are)*.

cvc word A word made up of three letters in the order consonant–vowel–consonant: for example, *cap, hut*.

derivation Where a word comes from and its original meaning: for example, *chef* comes from the French word meaning 'head' or 'chief'; *geology* comes from the ancient Greek words *geo*, meaning 'earth', and *logos*, meaning 'word'.

descender The part of a letter (such as *j* or *p*) that extends below the line.

homographs Words spelled the same way which are pronounced differently and have different meanings: for example, *Bow before the man with the bow tie*.

homonyms Words spelled the same way which have the same pronunciation but different meanings: for example, *We wave at the children as a wave rolls in*.

homophones Words that sound the same as one another, but are spelled differently and have different meanings: for example, *poor, pour, paw*.

letter string A sequence of letters that remains the same throughout spelling, although it may be pronounced differently in different words: for example, *ough* in *through, thought* and *cough*.

long vowel sound A vowel sound that 'says its name in the alphabet': for example, *ai* in *pain*, *o* in *cone* and *y* in *sky*.

mnemonic A personal way of remembering something: for example, *There's just ice in justice*.

noun A word that names a person, place or thing: for example, *a river, the Thames*.

phoneme The smallest unit of sound in a word. It is not necessarily a syllable and can be made up of one to four letters: for example, *dog* has the phonemes *d/o/g*; *though* has the phonemes *th/ough*.

possessive apostrophe An apostrophe used to denote something belonging to, or for, someone or something: for example, *the chair's legs, the ladies' cloakroom*.

prefix A group of letters attached to the beginning of a word which change the word's meaning: for example, *dis- (dis- + approve = disapprove); re- (re- + gain = regain)*. The word does not change spelling when a prefix is added.

root word A word to which prefixes and suffixes may be added: for example, *appear (dis- + appear + -ance = disappearance)*.

short vowel sound A vowel sound such as *a* in *pan*, *o* in *hot* and *u* in *up*.

suffix A group of letters attached to the end of a word which change the word's meaning and/or function: for example, *-ed (appear + -ed = appeared); -er (big + -er = bigger)*. The word may change spelling when a suffix is added.

syllable A rhythmic sound unit of a word. Each syllable should contain at least one vowel or a *y*: for example, *al/though* has two syllables; *syl/lab/le* has three.

synonyms Words with the same or similar meanings: for example, *joy, happiness, delight*.

unstressed vowel A vowel that is difficult to make out when spoken because it is uttered quickly or quietly: for example, *a* in *extraordinary*.

verb A word or group of words indicating action or a state of being: for example, *is, grow, reached*.

vowel phoneme A phoneme that makes a vowel sound: for example, *o* in *dog*, *ough* in *though*, *ea* in *lean* and *y* in *sky*.

vowel suffix A suffix that begins with a vowel or *y*: for example, *-ed, -ing, -able, -y*.

word family A group of words derived from the same root word: for example, *design, resign, signal* and *signature* (all from the root word *sign* and belonging to the same word family).

Developing Literacy: Word Level Year 8 © A & C BLACK